# Sharpen up their handwriting with CGP!

The best way for pupils to improve their handwriting skills in
Year Two (ages 6-7) is by doing as much practice as they can.

That's where this book comes in. It's packed with activities to help
them write neatly and get them used to joined-up writing.

And as you'd expect from CGP, everything's presented in a friendly
and colourful style to make learning to write as much fun as possible!

# What CGP is all about

Our sole aim here at CGP is to produce the highest quality books
— carefully written, immaculately presented and
dangerously close to being funny.

Then we work our socks off to get them out to you
— at the cheapest possible prices.

# Handwriting Hints

1. Sit up straight at your desk or at a table.

2. Get a grown-up to help you hold your pencil properly.
   Use your right or left hand — whichever you find easier.

3. Some pages have a big example of joined-up letters at the top.
   Use the red arrows to help you trace the join. Then you can
   practise the join with different letters on the lines underneath.

4. Use the lines to help you keep your letters neat.
   They will show you where your letters should sit and
   where the top and bottom of each letter should be.

5. Trace over the light blue letters and words first.
   Then copy them, using the red dots as a starting point.

6. Work neatly. Try and keep your letters the same size.

# Hints for Helpers

Here are a few things to bear in mind when using this book:
- Every school has its own handwriting style. Some schools may
  form letters and joins differently to how they're written here.
  Check with the school to see how they write and join each letter.
- As well as joined-up handwriting, this book covers break letters, which aren't joined
  to other letters. Some schools have different break letters (for example, g can be
  a break letter or it can be joined up). Check which break letters the school uses.
- Throughout the book, the red dots show where to start writing.
  As well as a red dot, the first example of each type of join also has arrows to follow.
- The book should be worked through in order — it gets harder as you go through,
  and builds on content covered earlier in the book.

# Contents

Published by CGP

*Editors*: Chris Corrall, Joanna Daniels, Caley Simpson
*Reviewer*: Anne James
With thanks to Karen Wells for the proofreading.

ISBN: 978 1 78294 696 0

Clipart from Corel®
Printed by Elanders Ltd, Newcastle upon Tyne.
Based on the classic CGP style created by Richard Parsons.

Text, design, layout and original illustrations © Coordination Group Publications Ltd. (CGP) 2016
All rights reserved.

Photocopying this book is not permitted. Extra copies are available from CGP with next day delivery.
0800 1712 712   •   www.cgpbooks.co.uk

# Alphabet Reminder

Get warmed up with a reminder of the whole alphabet.
Start at the red dot to trace and then copy each letter.

a　　　b　　　c

d　　　e　　　f　　　g

h　　　i　　　j　　　k　　　l

m　　　n　　　o　　　p

q　　　r　　　s　　　t

u　　　v　　　w

x　　　y　　　z

# Alphabet Holiday

Now practise tracing and copying these words about holidays.
Be careful — you've only got one starting dot for each word.

airport       beach

camp          diving    explore

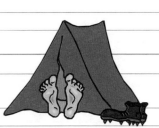

flying        globe

hotel         island

© CGP — not to be photocopied          *Year Two — Targeted Handwriting*

# Alphabet Holiday (Continued)

Here are some more words about holidays for you to trace and copy. Use the red dots to help you start each word.

jumbo jet

karting

luggage

map    nature

ocean    passport

quiet    rafting

© CGP — not to be photocopied

This is the last page of holiday words for you to trace and copy.

swimming  tickets

 underwater visit

walking  explore

yawn lazy

Did you fly through these holiday words?
Colour in one of the faces.

© CGP — not to be photocopied

*Year Two — Targeted Handwriting*

# The First Join

Start at the red dot
Follow the arrows to
join the **a** to the **r**.

Trace the join, then copy it. Start at the red dot each time.
Each join is made in the same way as the one above.

ar    *ar*

up    *up*

en    *en*

iv    *iv*

Now try joining from these tall letters.

hi    *hi*

lm    *lm*

© CGP — not to be photocopied

Practise the join by tracing these words, then copying them out underneath. Remember that all the joins are made the same way each time you do them.

lip aim     hum cup

him tin kip any air

dip dump     tiny imp

lump     mummy

How did you get on with this join?
Colour in a face to show how well you did.

# The Second Join

Trace the join between **c** and **h**. Start at the red dot and use the arrows to help you.

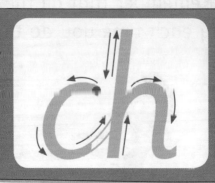

Copy out these joins to practise. The first one has been done for you. All these joins are made using the same pattern as the **ch** example.

ch *ch* · · · · ·

at *at* · · · · ·

ck *ck* · · · · ·

th *th* · · · · ·

Now try the join from an **e**. The join is still made in the same way.

el *el* · · · · ·

et *et* · · · · ·

© CGP — not to be photocopied

Trace each word first, then copy it out on the lines underneath. Start with your pencil on the red dot. Remember to go back and dot each **i** and cross each **t** and **f** after you finish the word.

tub    hit    ill    elf

knit    city    tilt    chill

think    kitty    chunk

until    dull    climb

Which of these faces shows how hard you found these pages? Colour it in!

© CGP — not to be photocopied

---

# The Third Join

Follow the arrows to trace over the join between **n** and **o**.

*no*

You'll need to go back on yourself to do the **o**.

Practise by tracing the joins first, then copying them out.

no   no

ng   ng

ea   ea

do   do

To join to **s**, you make the join in the same way, but it is longer. The **s** changes shape a bit too.

es   es

is   is

© CGP — not to be photocopied

Copy over these words then write them out underneath!
Start with your pencil on the red dot each time.

tag    had    and    into    dig

clam    licking    halt

adds    each    hats    muddy

launch    landing

Did you find these pages easy or hard?
Pick a face and colour it in!

# The Fourth Join

Starting at the red dot, follow the arrows to trace the join between **v** and **i**.

Remember to come back and dot the **i** after you finish!

These joins go from the top of one letter to the top of the next one.

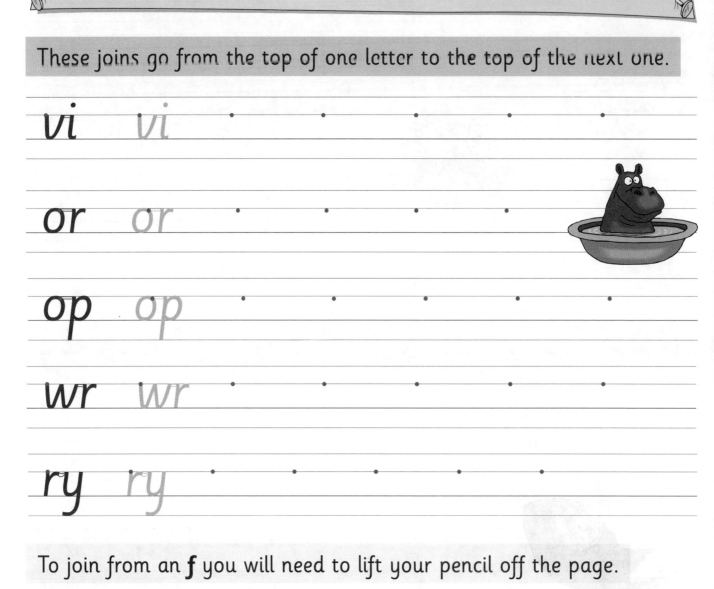

vi  *vi*

or  *or*

op  *op*

wr  *wr*

ry  *ry*

To join from an **f** you will need to lift your pencil off the page.

fr  *fr*

fi  *fi*

© CGP — not to be photocopied

First, trace the word. Then copy it out underneath.
The red dot shows you where to start.

our    arm    run    hop

rich    wing    fury

know    hurry    trim

living    fiction    villain

How did you get on with this join? Colour in a face!

© CGP — not to be photocopied    *Year Two — Targeted Handwriting*

# The Fifth Join

Start with your pencil on the red dot and follow the arrows to join **o** to **b**.

Make sure you go all the way to the bottom of the **b** before going back up to do the round bit.

Copy these joins. Use the red dots to help you.

The letter **f** is a bit different. Practise these joins.

*fl* *fl*

*ff* *ff*

    © CGP — not to be photocopied

Now practise joining these words.
Trace each word before you try copying it out.

fly    owl    loft    hawk

dark    murky    motor

lurking    fluffy    what

motion    dirty    violin

Colour in a face to show whether you found
this easy, not-so-easy or really hard!

© CGP — not to be photocopied    *Year Two — Targeted Handwriting*

# The Sixth Join

Trace over the letters to join **o** and **a**. Follow the arrows to help you.

When you're tracing the **a**, you'll have to go back over a bit you've already drawn.

Trace each join, then copy it out. Each one is done in the same way.

oa  *oa*

ws  *ws*

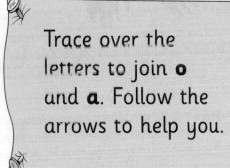

vo  *vo*

fa  *fa*

Now practise this join to letters with tails. The join is still made the same way.

rg  *rg*

oq  *oq*

© *CGP — not to be photocopied*

Now practise the joins in each of these words.
Trace over the word first, then copy it out underneath.

roll     frog     fat     cook

world     draws     foal

mirror     wrong     food

onwards     march     rowing

Did you find this join easy? Colour in
one of the faces to show how you got on.

© CGP — not to be photocopied     *Year Two — Targeted Handwriting*

# Joining to e

When you join from the bottom of a letter to an **e**, the **e** tilts slightly. Follow the arrows to try this join.

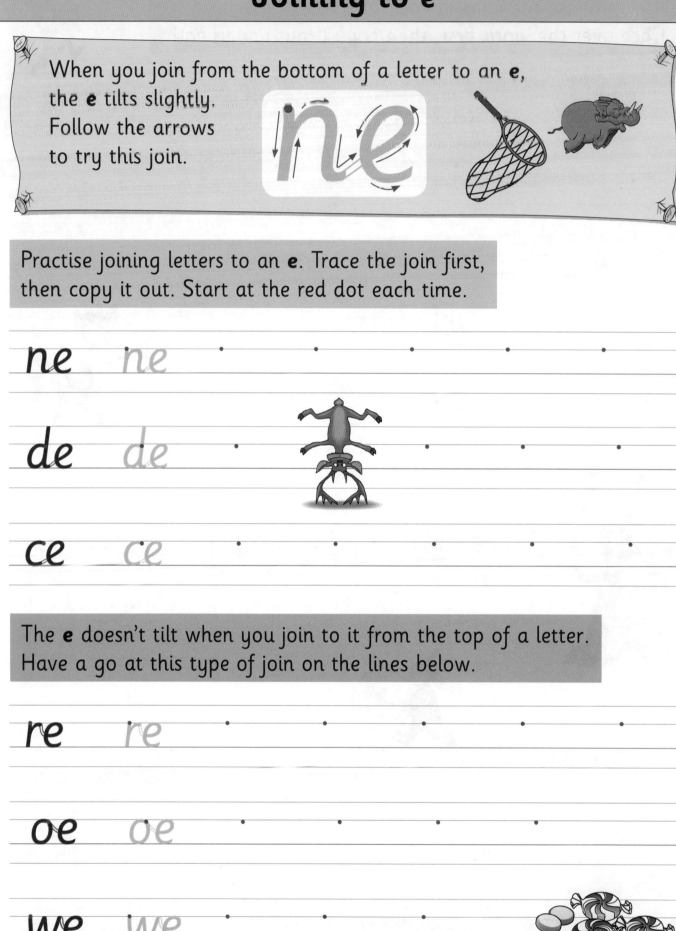

Practise joining letters to an **e**. Trace the join first, then copy it out. Start at the red dot each time.

ne    *ne*

de    *de*

ce    *ce*

The **e** doesn't tilt when you join to it from the top of a letter. Have a go at this type of join on the lines below.

re    *re*

oe    *oe*

we    *we*

The **ee** join is in a lot of words.
Practise the join on its own, then trace and copy the words.

*ee*    *ee*    .        .        .        .        .

*tree*    *knee*    *reef*    *wheel*

Now try tracing and copying these words.
You'll have to join to an **e** in all of them.

*toe*      *middle*    *funnier*

*wetter*    *camel*      *value*

Are you an expert at joining to the letter e?
Colour in the face that shows how you got on.

© CGP — not to be photocopied          *Year Two — Targeted Handwriting*

# Break Letters

Some letters aren't joined to the letters that come after them. They're called break letters. The break letters are:

# b g j p q s x y z

These words all start with break letters. Trace each word, then copy it out three times. Remember to join up the rest of the letters!

*giant*

*pencil*

*station*

*behind*

*yellow*

*jump*

This time, the break letters are in the middle of the words.
Trace and copy each word but watch out — some
of them have more than one break letter in them.

crying

require

energy

hospital

adjust

You don't join to or from the letters x and z.
Practise the letters by tracing and copying the words below.

mixing

crazy

quizzes

Colour in the face that shows how easy
or hard you found break letters.

# Capital Letter Practice

Capital letters never join to other letters.
Trace these names, then copy them out three times.

Holly

Elliot

Amani

Jake

Sophie

Now try these city names. Trace each one, then copy it out twice.
The red dots show you where to start each word.

London

Paris

New York

© CGP — not to be photocopied

Trace over each sentence, then copy it out underneath.
Remember, sentences always start with a capital letter.

Viv's birthday is in October.

Ravi is going to Wales next month.

Last week I went to Chester Zoo.

Mr Kang asked Ben to speak French.

How did you get on? Colour in one of
the faces to show how well you did.

© CGP — not to be photocopied    *Year Two — Targeted Handwriting*

# Handwriting Practice — A List

Trace this list of items to go in a party bag. Then copy each item on the lines underneath. Start at the red dot every time.

*a lollipop*

*two balloons*

*a sheet of stickers*

*a slice of birthday cake*

© CGP — not to be photocopied

# Handwriting Practice — An Advert

Here is an advert for a bike. Trace over each line,
then copy it underneath. Use the red dots to help you.

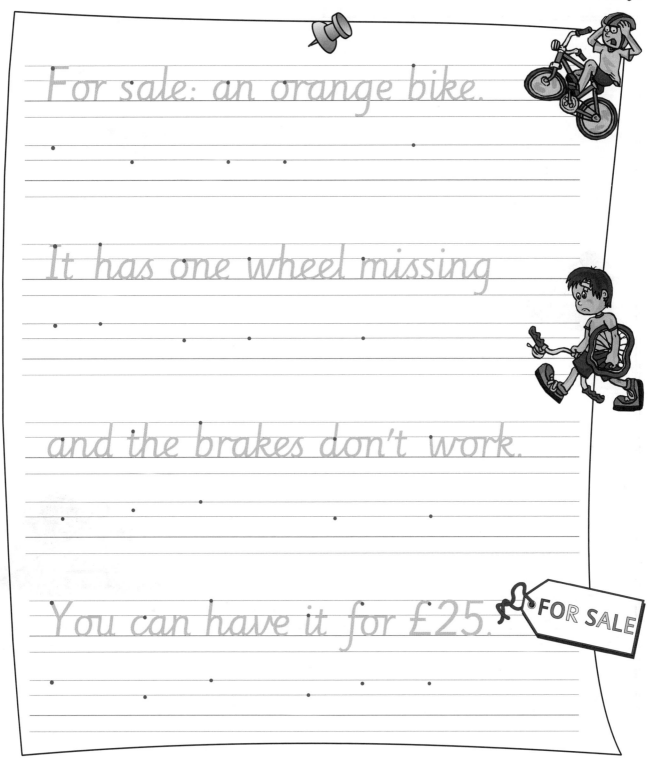

For sale: an orange bike.

It has one wheel missing

and the brakes don't work.

You can have it for £25.

How's your joined-up handwriting?
Colour in a face to show how you're getting on.

© CGP — not to be photocopied

*Year Two — Targeted Handwriting*

# Handwriting Practice — Rules

Trace these rules for a board game then copy them out underneath. The red dots show you where to start each word.

Rules

Roll the dice.

Move your counter forward.

Do what it says on the square.

  © CGP — not to be photocopied

# Handwriting Practice — A Message

A message in a bottle has washed up on the beach!
Trace then copy it, using the red dots to help you.

Help!

I'm stuck on a desert island.

My ship capsized in a storm.

Please send a search party.

Colour in one of the faces to show
how you got on with these pages.

© CGP — not to be photocopied  *Year Two — Targeted Handwriting*

# Handwriting Practice — A Riddle

Trace this riddle, then copy it out. You're only given the starting dot for each line so be careful. Can you work out the answer?

I spin when dropped

But always come back

I wrap round your finger

My string's rarely slack

Answer: a yo-yo

© CGP — not to be photocopied

# Handwriting Practice — A Fact Sheet

Here is some information about lions. Trace it first, then copy it out — the dots show you where to start each line.

Lions are a type of big cat.

Most lions are from Africa.

They live in groups called prides.

A female lion is called a lioness.

Colour in a face to show how well you did with only one starting dot for each line.

© CGP — not to be photocopied

*Year Two — Targeted Handwriting*

# Handwriting Practice — A Story

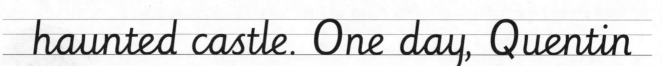

Here is the beginning of a story. Copy it out underneath.
What do you think might happen next?

Deep in the woods, there was a

.

haunted castle. One day, Quentin

.

and Uma felt brave enough to

.

explore the dark, spooky woods.

.

How did you do on the last page in the book?
Colour in one of the faces.

  © CGP — not to be photocopied